A DORLING KINDERSLEY BOOK

Senior Editor Jane Yorke
Editor Dawn Sirett
Senior Art Editor Mark Richards
Art Editor Jane Coney
Designer Karen Fielding
Production Marguerite Fenn

Photography by Tim Ridley
Illustrations by Jane Cradock-Watson and Dave Hopkins
Models by Conrad GMBH
Model consultant Ted Taylor

Eye Openers ®
First published in Great Britain in 1991
by Dorling Kindersley Limited,
9 Henrietta Street, London WC2E 8PS
Reprinted 1992, 1995

A CIP catalogue record for this book is
available from the British Library.

ISBN 0-86318-563-0

Reproduced by Colourscan, Singapore
Printed and bound in Italy by L.E.G.O., Vicenza

·EYE·OPENERS·

Diggers and Dumpers

Written by Angela Royston

DK

DORLING KINDERSLEY
London • New York • Stuttgart

Bulldozer

A bulldozer flattens the ground on a building site. Its blade pushes away earth and stones. Crawler tracks spread the bulldozer's weight to stop it from sinking into the mud.

D680E

exhaust
pipe

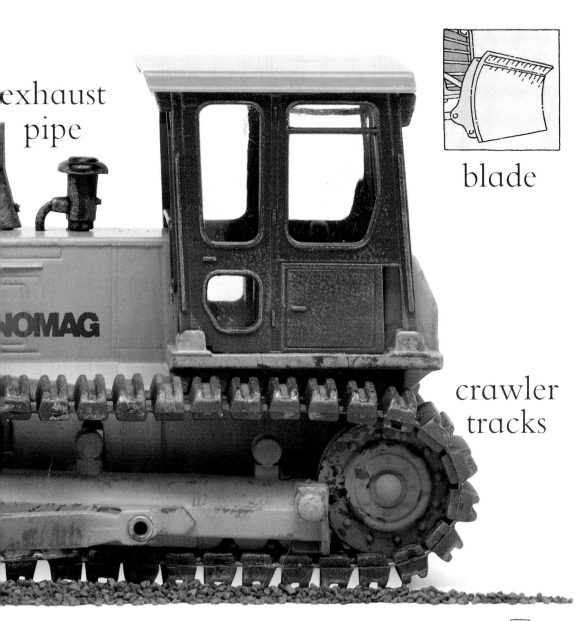

blade

NOMAG

crawler
tracks

Excavator

arm

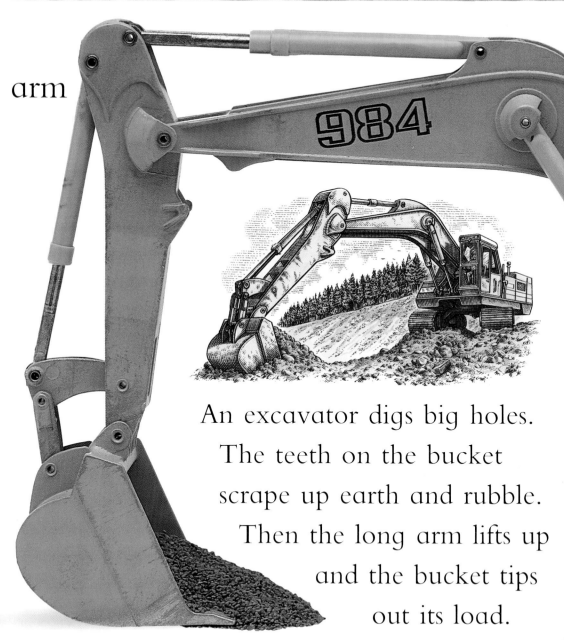

An excavator digs big holes.
The teeth on the bucket
scrape up earth and rubble.
Then the long arm lifts up
and the bucket tips
out its load.

8

cab   bucket   crawler tracks

9

Dumper truck

This dumper truck carries loads across the building site. It can tilt from side to side as it goes over the bumpy ground. The dumper body lifts up to let the earth slide out.

2366

wheel

10

exhaust
stack

steering
wheel

steps

dumper body

Digger

This digger can do two jobs. It has a bucket at the back and a shovel at the front. The bucket digs small holes, such as trenches for pipes. The shovel can push earth back over the pipes. The legs keep the digger steady.

shovel

mud-guard

leg

bucket

13

Tipper truck

A tipper truck brings loose materials like gravel or sand to the building site. When it's time to unload, powerful rams push up the tipper body. The tail-board at the back swings open. Then the load tumbles out into a pile.

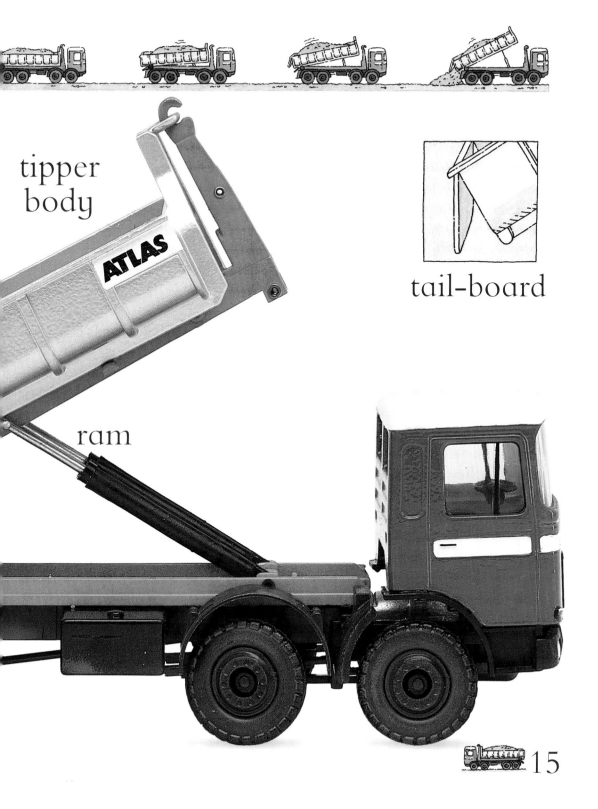

tipper
body

ATLAS

tail-board

ram

15

Wheel loader

A wheel loader carries bricks, wood, or pipes around the building site. It has a moving arm with long forks on the end. The driver uses levers in the cab to slide the forks under the heavy load. Then the load can be lifted up off the ground.

arm

forks

cab

levels

17

Tunnelling loader

This loader helps to dig tunnels. It scoops up the loose earth. The driver sits sideways. He can look forwards as he drives into the tunnel, or backwards when he drives out to dump the load. Powerful headlamps light his way.

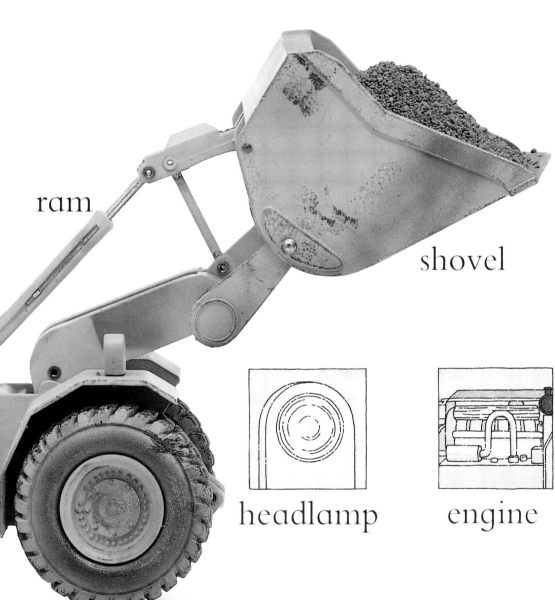

ram

shovel

headlamp

engine

 19

Giant dumper

This dumper truck is so big that the driver has to climb a ladder to reach the cab. Giant dumpers can carry heavy rocks and huge amounts of earth. They are used for building roads and tunnels.

20

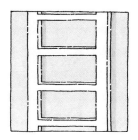

ladder

cab

dumper
body